SNOOPY

(features as)

The Great Philosopher

Charles M. Schulz

ℛℛ

Printed and bound in Great Britain
for Ravette Publishing Limited,
Unit 3, Tristar Centre,
Star Road, Partridge Green,
West Sussex RH13 8RA
by Cox & Wyman Ltd, Reading, Berkshire

ISBN: 1 84161 064 X

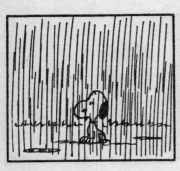

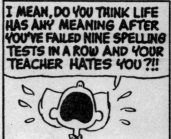

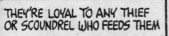

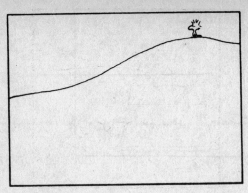

2-13

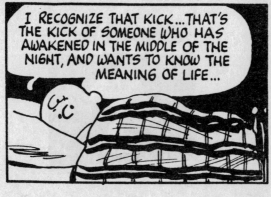

I RECOGNIZE THAT KICK...THAT'S THE KICK OF SOMEONE WHO HAS AWAKENED IN THE MIDDLE OF THE NIGHT, AND WANTS TO KNOW THE MEANING OF LIFE...

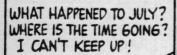

THE SECRET OF LIFE IS TO HANG AROUND PEOPLE WHO DON'T KNOW THE DIFFERENCE!

OR WHATEVER

DON'T STAY HERE...
THEY'LL COME AND GET
YOU WITH A RAKE..

© 1984 United Feature Syndicate, Inc.

9-29

NOBODY EVER
TELLS THEM
ABOUT THE
GUY WITH
THE RAKE..

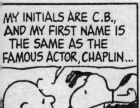

THAT'S STRANGE...I FEEL LIKE I'VE SEEN THAT DOG BEFORE..

ISN'T THERE AN EXPRESSION FOR THAT?

DÉJÀ BEAGLE!

Other PEANUTS titles published by Ravette ...

Snoopy Pocket Books
Snoopy features as ...   ISBN   Price

Man's Best Friend	1 84161 066 6	£2.99
Master of the Fairways	1 84161 067 4	£2.99
The Fitness Fanatic	1 84161 029 1	£2.99
The Flying Ace	1 84161 027 5	£2.99
The Legal Beagle	1 84161 065 8	£2.99
The Literary Ace	1 84161 026 7	£2.99
The Matchmaker	1 84161 028 3	£2.99

Snoopy's Laughter and Learning series
wipe clean pages
(a fun series of story and activity books for preschool
and infant school children)

Book 1 - Read with Snoopy	1 84161 016 X	£2.50
Book 2 - Write with Snoopy	1 84161 017 8	£2.50
Book 3 - Count with Snoopy	1 84161 018 6	£2.50
Book 4 - Colour with Snoopy	1 84161 019 4	£2.50

PEANUTS Anniversary Treasury
(224 pages featuring some of Charlie Brown's favourite
strips in colour and black & white)
                          1 84161 021 6   £9.99

You Really Don't Look 50 Charlie Brown
(over 500 daily and Sunday strips and a series of
Charles Schulz essays celebrating the anniversary year)

                          1 84161 020 8   £7.99

Prices are subject to change without prior notice.

All PEANUTS™ books are available from your local bookshop or from the address below. Just tick the titles required and send the form with your payment to:-

BBCS, P.O. Box 941, Kingston upon Hull HU1 3YQ
24-hr telephone credit card line 01482 224626

Prices and availability are subject to change without prior notice.

Please enclose a cheque or postal order made payable to BBCS to the value of the cover price of the book and allow the following for postage and packing:-

UK & BFPO:	£1.95 (weight up to 1kg)	3-day delivery
	£2.95 (weight over 1kg up to 20kg)	3-day delivery
	£4.95 (weight up to 20kg)	next day delivery
EU & Eire:	Surface Mail: £2.50 for first book & £1.50 for subsequent books	
	Airmail: £4.00 for first book & £2.50 for subsequent books	
USA:	Surface Mail: £4.50 for first book & £2.50 for subsequent books	
	Airmail: £7.50 for first book & £3.50 for subsequent books	
Rest of the World:	Surface Mail: £6.00 for first book & £3.50 for subsequent books	
	Airmail: £10.00 for first book & £4.50 for subsequent books	

Name: ....

Address: ....

....

....

Cards accepted: Visa, Mastercard, Switch, Delta, American Express

Expiry date .... Signature ....